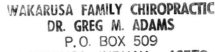

The Chiropractor Who Saved Christmas

Story by **Diane Miller**

Illustrations by **Ron Miller**

Published by
The Chiropractic Journal
2950 North Dobson Road, Suite 1
Chandler, Arizona 85524

Library of Congress, Cataloging in Publication Data
Miller, Diane
The Chiropractor Who Saved Christmas / Story by
Diane Miller / Illustrations by Ron Miller
p.   cm.

ISBN 0-9647168-8-7

1. Chiropractic. 2. Christmas. 3. Children.
4. Chiropractic Education. 5. Chiropractor.

Book Production by Marty Marsh Graphics & Design
Palm Springs, California

October 2004

10 9 8 7 6 5 4 3 2 1

To Aunt Linda, our
favorite chiropractor.

'Twas the night before Christmas

And at the North Pole

Santa and his reindeer

Were preparing to go.

When all of a sudden
Poor Dancer stopped dancing,
Dasher stopped dashing
And Prancer stopped prancing!

Santa was worried,
Confused and upset.
"Please, little elves,
Go and fetch me the vet!"

So the elves fetched the vet
And he came right away.
He checked out the reindeer
And had this to say:

"Dear Santa I wish that I knew
What to do, but I'm as confused
And as worried as you."

So they talked and they thought
In the warm little stall
When one little elf (so sweet and so small)
Quietly said, "I know who to call."

"It's May, and she lives
Just three houses down
In the little white cottage
At the edge of our town."

"But what can she do,"
Inquired St. Nick,
"So that my poor reindeer
Aren't feeling so sick?"

"May is a chiropractor,
She'll adjust the spine."
Said the sweet little elf,
"Why, she's done it to mine!

They're just out of alignment
From all that they do.
And I think," he said shyly,
"Santa, you need this, too."

Santa thought for a moment
Then stated with haste,
"Well, call her right over!
We've no time to waste!"

So the elves fetched May

And she came right away,

And while she greeted the reindeer

She heard Santa say:

"Let's get this show moving!
Let's get underway!
It's almost time
To leave with the sleigh!

The world really
needs us,
The children are
waiting.
So let's get in line for
Some health May's
creating."

"Um, Santa," May ventured,
"Our health comes from inside.
I just help with alignment
So your sickness can't hide.

You create your own health,

You create how you feel.

I help open the channels

So your body can heal.

We all have a gift, it is really quite neat!
The world's like a puzzle we all help to complete.

Yours is with presents and kindness and giving.
I share an adjustment and a new zest for living!"

Santa smiled at May

And gave her a wink.

"Dr. May," Santa chuckled,

"I like how you think!"

So they all
    lined up quickly
In a neat
    little row.

There was excitement among them
When it was their turn to go.

It got quiet while May
Adjusted each little elf,
And the vet, then the reindeer
And, yes, Santa himself.

They were amazed at her gift
And her gentle touch,
And when each one was finished
Santa said, "Thank you SO much."

May put on her coat
And folded her table,
And said this to Santa
Before leaving the stable:

"One Christmas you'll look down
From your sleigh up above,
And you'll see that the whole world
Is filled up with love.

And you'll wink and you'll smile
When you see this come true.
It's a little of me,
And a little of you."

Santa's eyes twinkled
(And May's twinkled, too)
With each of them knowing
The job they must do.

With that the reindeer
Were ready to go.
And up on the rooftop
It started to snow.

May said her farewells

And walked home through the night

And she knew, for that moment,

In the world, all was right.